Date: 29 July — 3 Aug. WK1
2008

Exercises/scales:

Dates

Pieces:
Titles

GW00643922

Other work:
(sight-reading, theory, aurals etc)

S·R

Theory

This week's lesson:
(Teacher, tick the box!)

Date:

Exercises/scales:

Pieces:

Other work:
(sight-reading, theory, aurals etc)

This week's lesson:
(Teacher, tick the box!)

Excellent	Quite good	Not so good!
☐	☐	☐

Date: /   Wk 3

Exercises/scales:

Pieces:

Other work:
(sight-reading, theory, aurals etc)

This week's lesson:
(Teacher, tick the box!)

Excellent

Quite good

Not so good!

Date:

Exercises/scales:

Pieces:

Other work:
(sight-reading, theory, aurals etc)

This week's lesson:
(Teacher, tick the box!)

Excellent	Quite good	Not so good!
☐	☐	☐

Date: Wk 5

Exercises/scales:

Pieces:

Other work:
(sight-reading, theory, aurals etc)

This week's lesson:
(Teacher, tick the box!)

Excellent	Quite good	Not so good!

Date: Wk 6

Exercises/scales:

Pieces:

Other work:
(sight-reading, theory, aurals etc)

This week's lesson:
(Teacher, tick the box!)

Excellent

Quite good

Not so good!

Date:

Exercises/scales:

Pieces:

Other work:
(sight-reading, theory, aurals etc)

This week's lesson:
(Teacher, tick the box!)

Excellent	Quite good	Not so good!

Date:

Exercises/scales:

Pieces:

Other work:
(sight-reading, theory, aurals etc)

This week's lesson:
(Teacher, tick the box!)

Excellent	Quite good	Not so good!
☐	☐	☐

Date:

Exercises/scales:

Pieces:

Other work:
(sight-reading, theory, aurals etc)

This week's lesson:
(Teacher, tick the box!)

Excellent	Quite good	Not so good!
☐	☐	☐

Date:

Exercises/scales:

Pieces:

Other work:
(sight-reading, theory, aurals etc)

This week's lesson:
(Teacher, tick the box!)

Excellent	Quite good	Not so good!
☐	☐	☐

Date:

Exercises/scales:

Pieces:

Other work:
(sight-reading, theory, aurals etc)

This week's lesson:
(Teacher, tick the box!)

Excellent	Quite good	Not so good!
☐	☐	☐

Date:

Exercises/scales:

Pieces:

Other work:
(sight-reading, theory, aurals etc)

This week's lesson:
(Teacher, tick the box!)

Excellent	Quite good	Not so good!
☐	☐	☐

Date:

Exercises/scales:

Pieces:

Other work:
(sight-reading, theory, aurals etc)

This week's lesson:
(Teacher, tick the box!)

Excellent

Quite good

Not so good!

Date:

Exercises/scales:

Pieces:

Other work:
(sight-reading, theory, aurals etc)

This week's lesson:
(Teacher, tick the box!)

Excellent   Quite good   Not so good!

Date:

Exercises/scales:

Pieces:

Other work:
(sight-reading, theory, aurals etc)

This week's lesson:
(Teacher, tick the box!)

Excellent	Quite good	Not so good!
☐	☐	☐

Date:

Exercises/scales:

Pieces:

Other work:
(sight-reading, theory, aurals etc)

This week's lesson:
(Teacher, tick the box!)

Excellent   Quite good   Not so good!

Date:

Exercises/scales:

Pieces:

Other work:
(sight-reading, theory, aurals etc)

This week's lesson:
(Teacher, tick the box!)

Excellent

Quite good

Not so good!

Date:

Exercises/scales:

Pieces:

Other work:
(sight-reading, theory, aurals etc)

This week's lesson:
(Teacher, tick the box!)

Excellent	Quite good	Not so good!
☐	☐	☐

Date:

Exercises/scales:

Pieces:

Other work:
(sight-reading, theory, aurals etc)

This week's lesson:
(Teacher, tick the box!)

Excellent	Quite good	Not so good!
☐	☐	☐

Date:

Exercises/scales:

Pieces:

Other work:
(sight-reading, theory, aurals etc)

This week's lesson:
(Teacher, tick the box!)

Excellent	Quite good	Not so good!
☐	☐	☐

Date:

Exercises/scales:

Pieces:

Other work:
(sight-reading, theory, aurals etc)

This week's lesson:
(Teacher, tick the box!)

Excellent	Quite good	Not so good!
☐	☐	☐

Date:

Exercises/scales:

Pieces:

Other work:
(sight-reading, theory, aurals etc)

This week's lesson:
(Teacher, tick the box!)

Excellent	Quite good	Not so good!
☐	☐	☐

Date:

Exercises/scales:

Pieces:

Other work:
(sight-reading, theory, aurals etc)

This week's lesson:
(Teacher, tick the box!)

Excellent	Quite good	Not so good!
☐	☐	☐

Date:

Exercises/scales:

Pieces:

Other work:
(sight-reading, theory, aurals etc)

This week's lesson:
(Teacher, tick the box!)

Excellent	Quite good	Not so good!
☐	☐	☐